THE MONTHS OF THE YEAR

Sara Coleridge

January brings the snow;
Makes the toes and fingers glow.

February brings the rain,
Thaws the frozen ponds again.

March brings the breezes loud and shrill,
Stirs the dancing daffodil.

April brings the primrose sweet,
Scatters daisies at our feet.

May brings flocks of pretty lambs,
Skipping by their fleecy dams.

June brings tulips, lilies, roses;
Fills the children's hands with posies.

Hot July brings cooling showers,
Strawberries and gilly-flowers.

August brings the sheaves of corn,
Then the Harvest home is borne.

Warm September brings the fruit,
Sportsmen then begin to shoot.

Fresh October brings the pheasant;
Then to gather nuts is pleasant.

Dull November brings the blast,
Then the leaves are falling fast.

Chill December brings the sleet,
Blazing fire and Christmas treat.

Proverb and Calendar Illustrations by Cheryl Chalmers

Paintings by Robert Goldstrom

QuillMark

A Division of Random House, Inc.

LYNN HOLLYN

BOOK OF DAYS

Published in the United States by QuillMark,
a division of Random House, Inc., New York.
This product manufactured by QuillMark™
under license from
Lynn Hollyn Associates, Incorporated
ISBN 0-866-81365-9
Manufactured in the United States of America

To all of those we love and
wish to remember

Treasure this Book of Days
as a keepsake album of special
moments, memories, and occasions

THE SMALLEST FELINE IS A MASTERPIECE

JANUARY

1
2
3
4
5
6
7
8
9
10
11
12
13
14
15
16

17
18
19
20
21
22
23
24
25
26
27
28
29
30
31

No Workman
Can Build a Door
Proof Against a
Cat or a Lover

FEBRUARY

1	15
2	16
3	17
4	18
5	19
6	20
7	21
8	22
9	23
10	24
11	25
12	26
13	27
14	28

I love Cats because
I love my Home
And after awhile they become
Its visible Soul

MARCH

1

2

3

4

5

6

7

8

9

10

11

12

13

14

15

16

17

18

19

20

21

22

23

24

25

26

27

28

29

30

31

a little lion
small and dainty sweet
with sea-grey eyes
and softly stepping feet

April

1 ____
2 ____
3 ____
4 ____
5 ____
6 ____
7 ____
8 ____
9 ____
10 ____
11 ____
12 ____
13 ____
14 ____
15 ____
16 ____
17 ____
18 ____
19 ____
20 ____
21 ____
22 ____
23 ____
24 ____
25 ____
26 ____
27 ____
28 ____
29 ____
30 ____

Puss on the hearth
with velvet paws
Sits wiping o'er his
whiskered jaws.

May

1
2
3
4
5
6
7
8
9
10
11
12
13
14
15
16
17
18
19
20
21
22
23
24
25
26
27
28
29
30
31

TO RESPECT THE CAT IS THE
BEGINNING OF THE AESTHETIC SENSE

JUNE

1	16
2	17
3	18
4	19
5	20
6	21
7	22
8	23
9	24
10	25
11	26
12	27
13	28
14	29
15	30

Cats winged yearnings journey
Unrestrained
oer time and space

July

1
2
3
4
5
6
7
8
9
10
11
12
13
14
15
16
17
18
19
20
21
22
23
24
25
26
27
28
29
30
31

Je salue en toi calme penseur
deux exquises vertus
scepticism et douceur

AUGUST

1
2
3
4
5
6
7
8
9
10
11
12
13
14
15
16
17
18
19
20
21
22
23
24
25
26
27
28
29
30
31

There is, indeed, no single quality of the cat that man could not emulate to his advantage

September

1
2
3
4
5
6
7
8
9
10
11
12
13
14
15
16
17
18
19
20
21
22
23
24
25
26
27
28
29
30

In a Cats Eye all things belong to Cats

October

1
2
3
4
5
6
7
8
9
10
11
12
13
14
15
16
17
18
19
20
21
22
23
24
25
26
27
28
29
30
31

The
world is so full
of a number of mice
I'm sure that we all
should be happy
and nice

NOVEMBER

1
2
3
4
5
6
7
8
9
10
11
12
13
14
15
16
17
18
19
20
21
22
23
24
25
26
27
28
29
30

A cat
maie looke
on a king
ye know

December

1
2
3
4
5
6
7
8
9
10
11
12
13
14
15
16

17
18
19
20
21
22
23
24
25
26
27
28
29
30
31

SPECIAL MEMORIES

SPECIAL MEMORIES

Time, indeed, is a sacred gift, and
each day is a little life.

—John Lubbock

Proverbs: January-Leonardo Da Vinci. February-French saying. March-John Cocteau. April-Graham Tomson. May-"The Nation." June-Erasmus Darwin. July-Hiddigeigei. August-Jules Lemaître. September-Carl Van Vechten. October-English saying. November-Oliver Herford. December-John Heywood.